Beautiful
COLOUR BY NUMBERS

Beautiful
COLOUR BY NUMBERS

Compiled by **Felicity James**

ARCTURUS

Illustrations by Else Lennox,
Arpad Olbey, Nathalie Ortega,
Martin Sanders, Sara Storino
and David Woodroffe.

This edition published in 2020 by Arcturus Publishing Limited
26/27 Bickels Yard, 151–153 Bermondsey Street,
London SE1 3HA

ISBN: 978-1-78888-768-7
CH006905NT
Supplier 29, Date 1219, Print run 9996

Printed in China

Created for children 10+

Introduction

We all get the urge to be creative from time to time, but often we don't know where to start. This collection of colour-by-number images is designed to make the first steps easier, setting you on a path to creating artworks you can be proud of. You don't need to think about what to draw or worry about how to draw it – just choose an image and get stuck in. The colour-by-numbers format can boost your colouring skills and dexterity, as well as improving your concentration.

The world is full of exciting subjects for the artist, and this collection contains over sixty ideas for you to choose from. Whether you want to depict the serene beauty of Mount Fuji, the simple joy of a bunch of flowers or the warm glow of a café at night, there will be something to fire your imagination. Also among these pages are several intricate patterns for colouring, including the circular mandala patterns that are used to represent the universe in Hindu and Buddhist symbolism.

Each image is fully numbered so that you can build up an impressive artwork. Using the colour key on the cover, match your set of coloured pencils to the colours in the key. If there is no number that means the space should be left white or coloured with a white pencil.

It can be hugely rewarding to indulge your creative side, and who knows where it will take you?

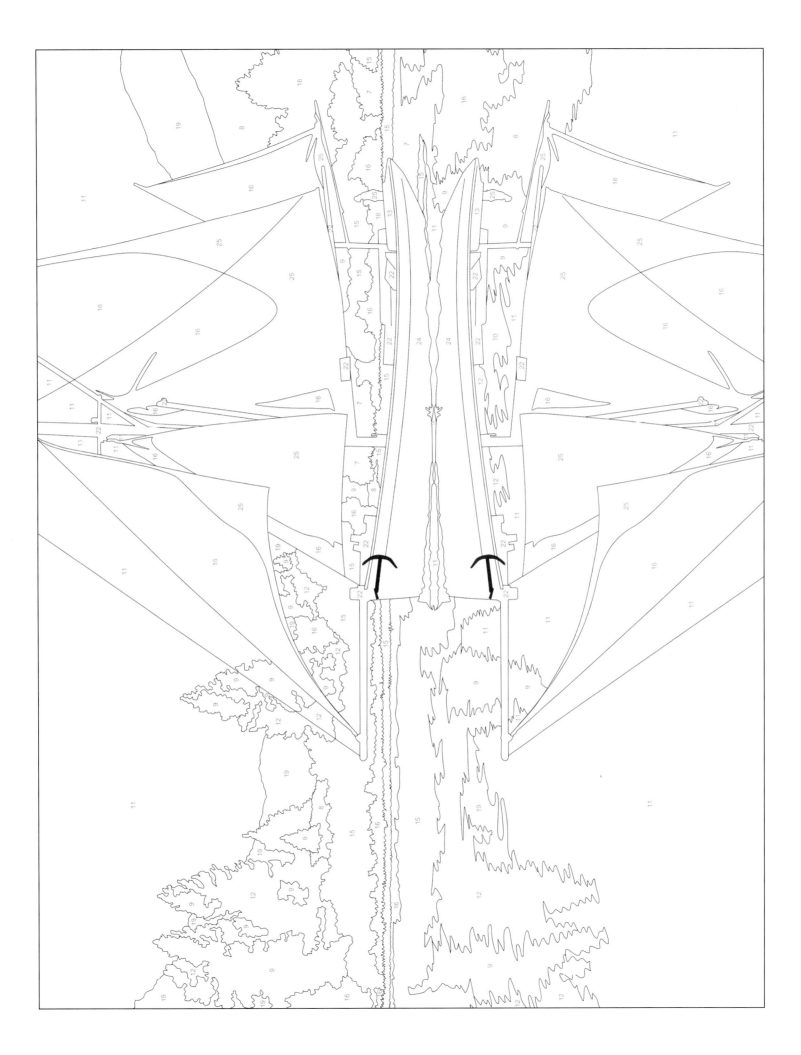

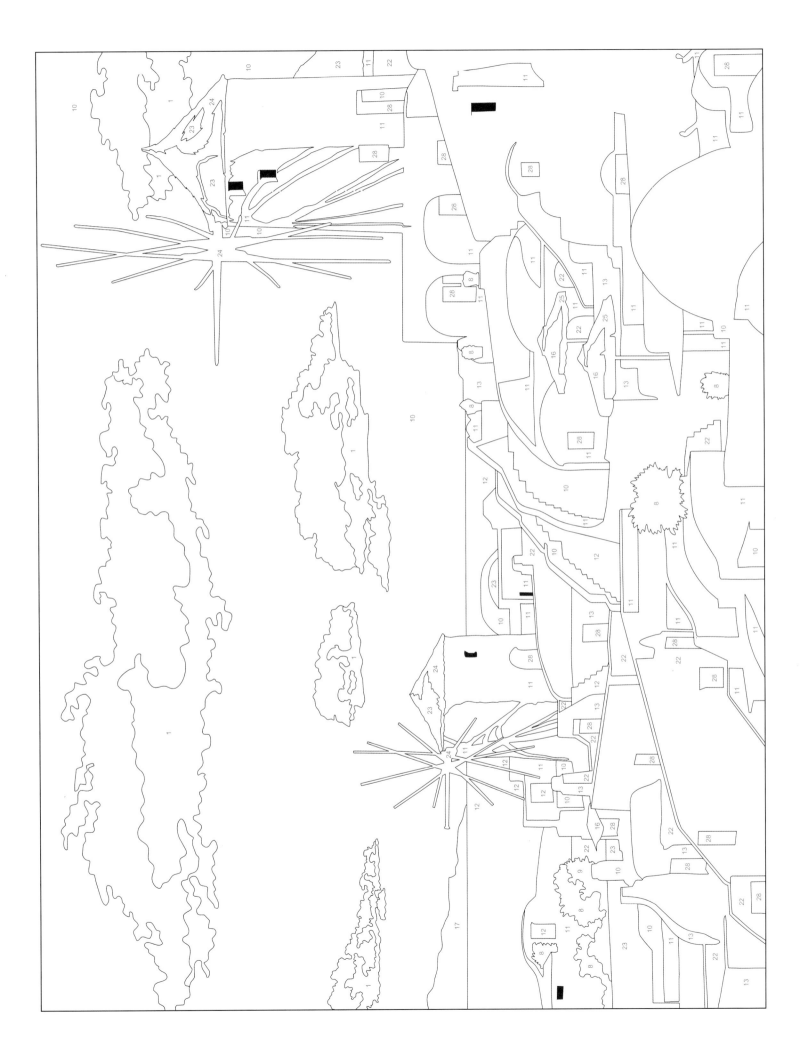